Help with Homework
Handwriting

bone

car

apple

door

Writing trails

Start at the dots and follow the lines to complete these writing trails.

Writing patterns

Trace and finish the writing patterns on this poster.
Start at the top and work from left to right.

Writing patterns

Trace and finish the writing patterns these aeroplanes have made.
Write your own pattern for the aeroplane at the bottom of the page.

The alphabet

Trace and copy the letters of the alphabet.

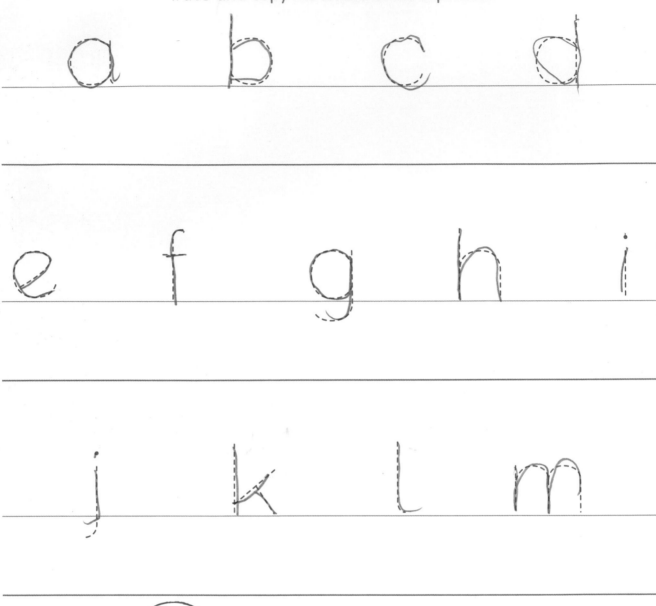

a   b   c   d

e   f   g   h   i

j   k   l   m

n o p q

r s t u v

w x y z

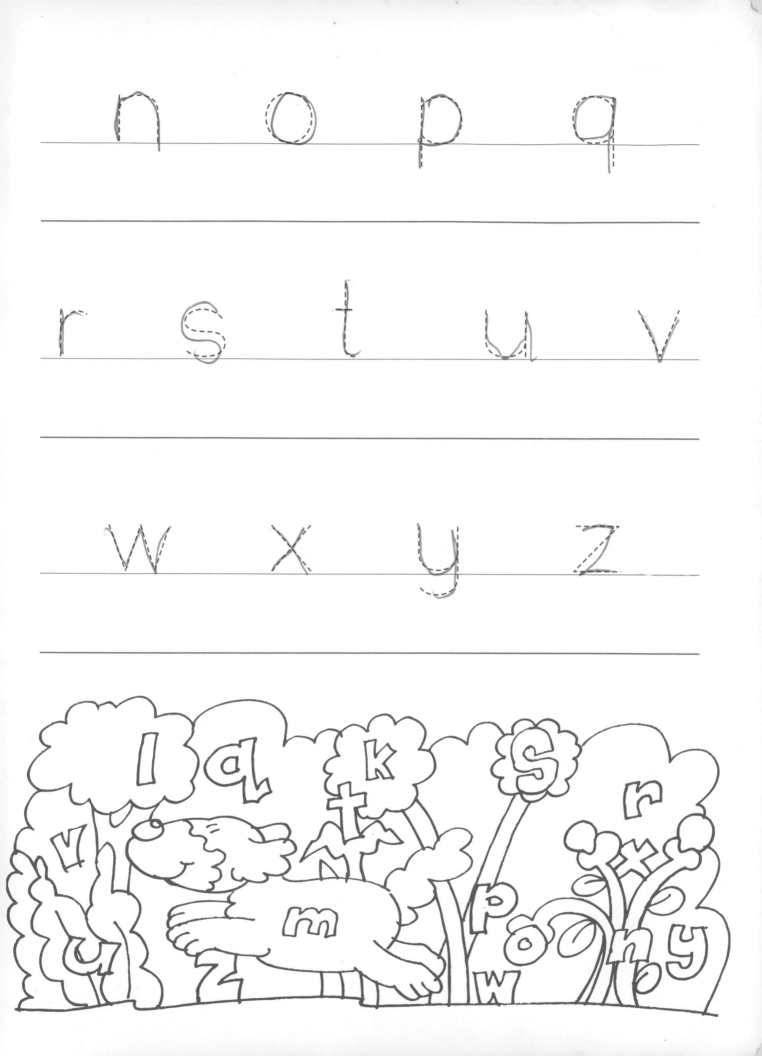

Joining strokes

To do joined-up writing you add **exit** strokes at the base of some letters.
Trace these letters and then write them yourself.

i l k u m

i l k u m

n a d e t c

n a d e t c

Practise

Write a row of each of these words.

made _made_____

tale _tale_____

milk _milk_____

nail _____

talk _____

came _____

Joining strokes

Letters based on a half-circle or circle, have joining strokes at the **beginning**.
Trace the letters and then write them yourself.

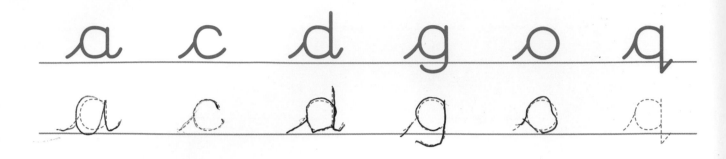

a   c   d   g   o   q

Practise: ad   do   oc   ag

Practise

Write a row of each of these words.

dog   *dog*

gone   *gone*

gate   *gate*

cat   *cat*

quiet   *quiet*

out

Joining strokes

Some letters have **exit** strokes at the top of the letter.
Trace the letters and then write them yourself.

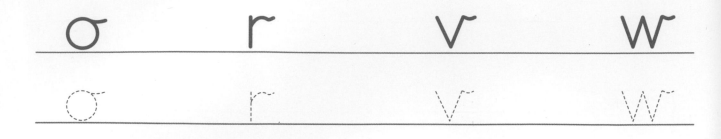

o   r   v   w

o   r   v   w

Practise: oo   rrr   vv   ww

oo   rrr   vv   ww

Practise

Write a row of each of these words.

word _word_

vase _vase_

how _how_

race _race_

were _were_

row _row_

Joining strokes

The letters **f** and **t** sometimes have different kinds of joining strokes.
Trace the letters and then write them yourself.

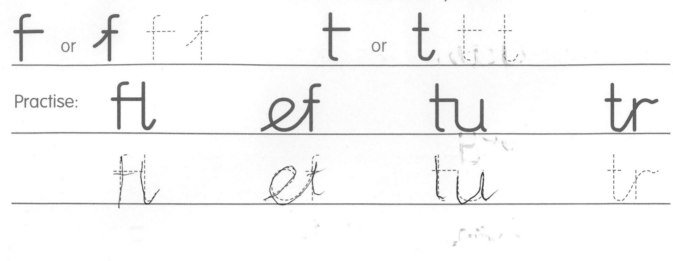

Practise:

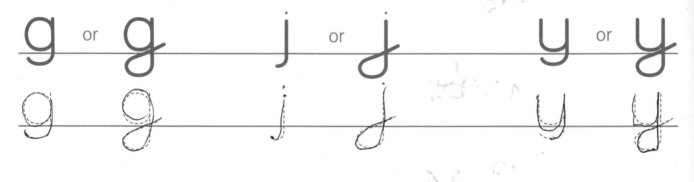

Some letters can be joined with a loop, or they can be left unjoined.

Practise

Write a row of each of these words.

gate   *gate*   *gate*

joy   *joy*   *joy*

feet   *feet*   *feet*

try   *try*   *try*

yolk   *yolk*   *yolk*

grow   *grow*   *grow*

Joining strokes

This is how to join all the remaining letters in the alphabet.
These letters can be joined or left unjoined. Trace the letters and then write them yourself.

p   b   z   x   s

ph   br   bl

ph   br   bl

ox   box   zoo

ox   box   zoo

Practise

Write a row of each of these words.

zip _____

past _____

clip _____

fox _____

buzz _____

six _____

Capital letters

Use the arrows to help you write the alphabet in capital letters.

N O P Q

R S T U V

W X Y Z

Using capital letters

Write the initial letters of these names in capital letters.

claire smith   jamie watson

_____   _____

steven david rogers

_____

Write the initial letters of this address in capital letters.

rose cottage
cedar road
guildford
surrey

_____

_____

_____

_____

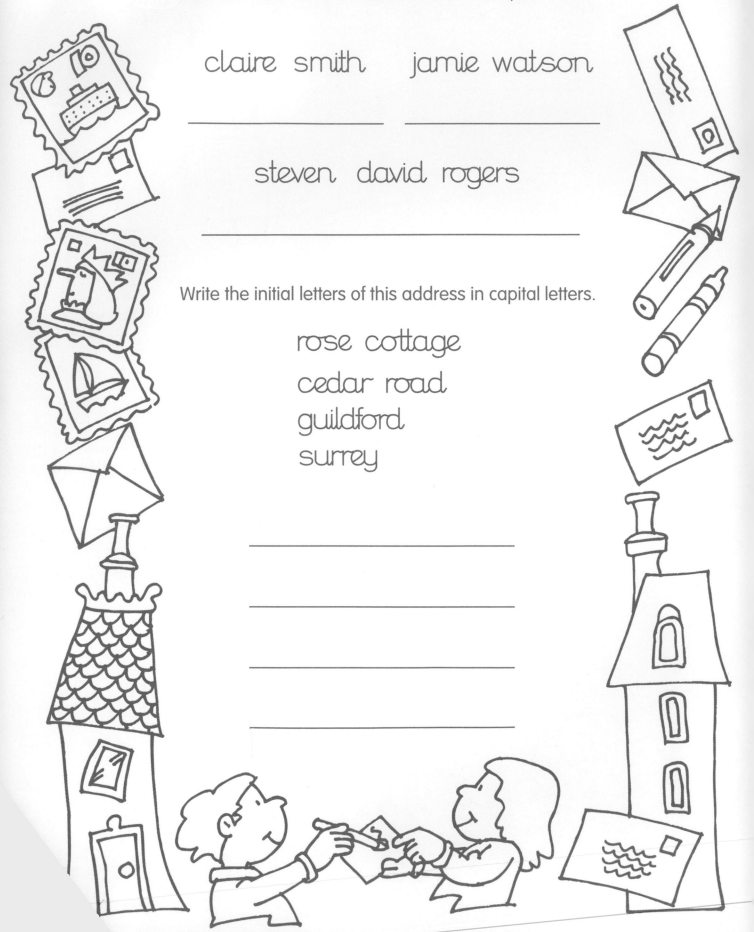

Writing days and months

Days of the week and months of the year also begin with capital letters.
Write the initial letters of the month and days as capital letters.
Then copy the diary entry for each day.

january _____

monday _____

I got an 'A' for my maths homework.

_____

tuesday _____

I went swimming after school with John.

_____

wednesday _____

I practised for my recorder exam.

_____

Writing numbers

Finish writing the number words from 1 to 20.

one   two   three

Rhyming words

Write these words in your neatest handwriting.
Draw lines to join the pairs of words that rhyme.

goose _____   game _____

lent _____   bean _____

free _____   fly _____

blame _____   loose _____

try _____   call _____

ball _____   trough _____

green _____   bent _____

cough _____   bee _____

Copy phrases

Copy each rhyming phrase in your best handwriting.

one dog on a log

two bats wearing hats

three bees all at sea

four snakes eating cakes

five sheep in a heap

six moles in holes

seven bugs in a rug ✓

eight cats on mats

nine bears in flares

ten mice eating rice

eleven frogs wearing clogs

twelve pigs in wigs

Copy and complete

Using the words at the top of the page,
copy and complete these rhyming sentences in your best handwriting.

well sea van down toy girl

The clown fell .

The boy dropped his

The shell is on a .

The  found a pearl.

The man drove a .

The tree is by the .

Copy and complete

Using the words at the top of the page, copy and complete these phrases.

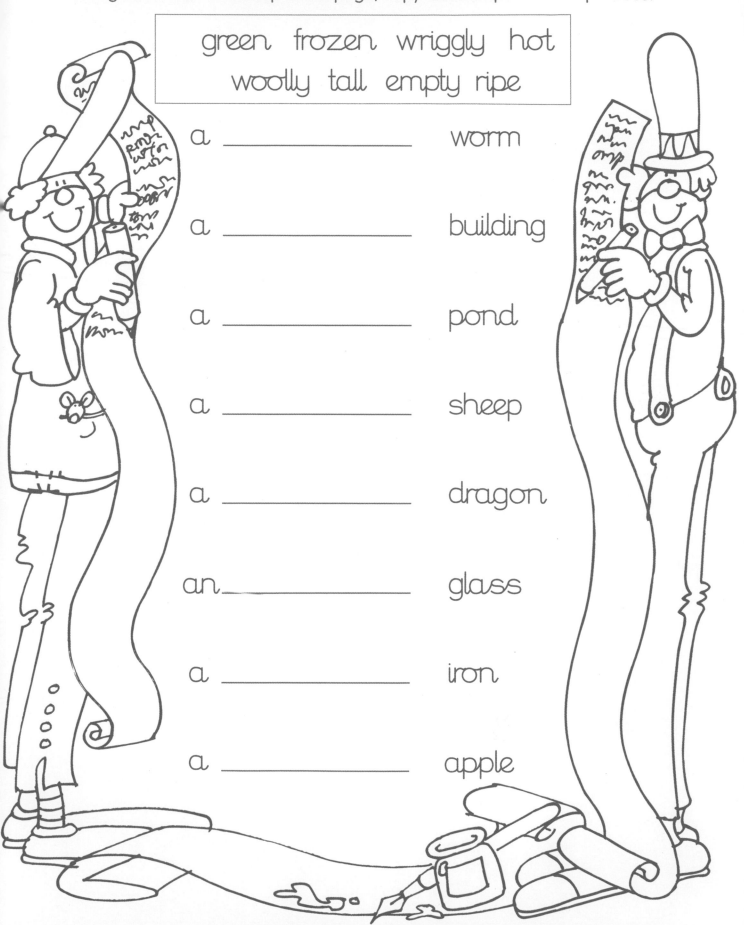

green frozen wriggly hot
woolly tall empty ripe

a _____ worm

a _____ building

a _____ pond

a _____ sheep

a _____ dragon

an _____ glass

a _____ iron

a _____ apple

Writing sentences

Copy these sentences in your best handwriting.

The children pointed at the beautiful rainbow.

_____

_____

It took him a long time to reach his house.

_____

_____

The heavy snow made it difficult to see the cars.

_____

_____

She took a deep breath and jumped in.

_____

_____

Writing sentences

Copy these sentences in your best handwriting.

He looked for the word in the dictionary.

_____

_____

Sarah ran down the stairs and opened her present.

_____

_____

"Where are you going?" asked Ben.

_____

_____

The dog dug deep in search of his bone.

_____

_____

Write a poem

Copy the verse from this poem by Edward Lear in your best handwriting.

The Table and the Chair

Said the Table to the Chair,

'You can hardly be aware,

'How I suffer from the heat,

'And from chilblains on my feet!

'If we took a little walk,

'We might have a little talk!

'Pray let us take the air!'

Said the Table to the Chair.

Writing a postcard

Imagine you are on holiday.
In your best handwriting, write a postcard to your friend.
Write the name and address on the lines under the stamp.

Dear _____

From _____

Reading and Writing

1. Tom's car was really fast.

2. The wheel came off.

3. A quick pitstop.

4. Ready to race again!

Out and about

Fill in the missing letters on these signs.

A sleepy surprise

This story has gotten mixed up.
Put the story in order by writing the letters in the boxes at the bottom of the page.

A Freddie called his friends over to take a look.

B Suddenly, he noticed a pair of eyes staring at him.

C It was an ordinary morning at the fire station.

D Freddie Fizz was polishing his shiny red fire engine.

E But the fox was frightened and ran back to the fields.

F There, curled up in the corner, was a fox!

1 ☐ 2 ☐ 3 ☐ 4 ☐ 5 ☐ 6 ☐

Good spells!

Wanda Witch has written the ingredients for her favourite spells.
Write them in your neatest handwriting, but be sure to correct her spelling!

whing of bat

skin of snaike

whiska of kitten

shoo of horse

tode slime

snaill shell

wool of lam

green custerd

milk of gote

mane of lyon

tale of rat

egg of oztrich

peacock fether

toe nales

webb of spyder

tooth of dragen

Fairy-tale postcards

Use your imagination to finish writing these fairy-tale postcards.
The first one has been done for you.

Dear Snow White,

How are you? The seven of us miss
you very much. Grumpy has been
really grumpy and Happy has been
really sad!
Write back to us soon.

Lots of love,

The Seven Dwarfs

Snow White

The Enchanted Castle

High Mountains

Magical Kingdom

MK3 5Az

Dear Tom Thumb,

_____

_____

_____

_____

_____

Master Tom Thumb

_____

_____

_____

Hi Grandma,

_____

_____

_____

_____

Grandma

_____

_____

_____

Love,
Little Red Riding Hood

Dear Rapunzel,
_____
_____
_____
_____
_____
_____

Miss Rapunzel
Tall Tower
Dark Forest
Faraway Land
FL2 6AT

Dear Hansel,
_____
_____
_____
_____
_____

Master Hansel
_____
_____
_____

Dear Rumpelstiltskin,
_____
_____
_____
_____
_____
_____

Rumpelstiltskin
_____
_____
_____

Magic symbols

The Great Alphonso has made the punctuation magically disappear
from these sentences. Rewrite the sentences, punctuating them correctly.
You will need the following:

?	5 question marks	A	23 capital letters
!	3 exclamation marks	,	4 commas
"	18 speech marks	.	14 full stops

can you go to the store for me his mother asked

----

lizzie john and anna took the dog for a walk

----

it was fantastic he yelled

----

why does this always happen to me laughed jasmine

----

the twins told their brother they were going to be late

----

are you travelling on this train patrick asked

----

watch out he shouted

she turned the corner and ran into the house

----

why do I have to do this gwen asked

----

would she get there on time

----

they grabbed their bags coats and books

----

maria said i can't wait to go on holiday

----

it was not long before they heard the sound again

----

look at the snow cried mark

----

frank turned and said you have to move your car

Up, up and away

Write a story to go with these pictures.
The first one has been done for you.

1. Colin and Claire have always

wanted to take a balloon ride.

2.

3.

4.

5.

6.

7. _____

8. _____

9. _____

10. _____

11. _____

12. _____

Lights, camera, action!

There are two different storylines hidden in this passage.
Direct the story by circling the words you want to use.
The pictures are clues.

Washington Smith saw the **emerald/fish** he had been searching for, shining in the **eyes/lid** of a huge **freezer/statue**. He gently eased himself through the **tunnel/aisle** and reached down into the **freezer/statue**. With a steady hand, he carefully lifted the **emerald/fish** out and placed it in his empty **shopping trolley/pocket**. He began to hear a **squeaking/rumbling** sound. "Aargh!" he screamed, as a runaway **boulder/shopping trolley** came hurtling down the **tunnel/aisle** towards him. As he fell to the floor, the **fish/emerald** slipped from his grasp and flew through the air, falling into the **lair/lap** of the angry **cashier/dragon**.

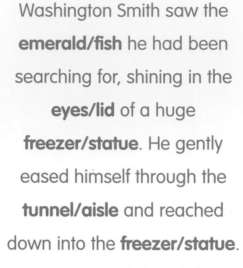

Flapjacks

Look at the pictures of these children making flapjacks.
Write the instructions to go with them.
The first one has been done for you.

1. Grease a shallow cake tin

with a little butter.

2. _____

_____

3. _____

_____

4. _____

_____

5. _____

_____

6. _____

_____

Vinnie the Vowel Muncher

Vinnie the Vowel Muncher has munched some of the vowels in this paragraph.
Add the missing vowels.

Vinnie was very hungry and munched s_me _f th_ v_wels in th_s pi_ce of writ_ng. He nev_r w_nt to sch_ol _nd d_es not kn_w h_w m_ny vow_ls ther_ ar_ in the _lph_bet. V_wels jo_n th_ oth_r l_tters t_geth_r. Th_re ar_ v_ry f_w w_rds that do n_t h_ve _t le_st on_ vow_l. Lo_k _t th_ w_y th_ vow_ls beh_ve wh_n yo_ re_d. The_r so_nds c_n ch_nge fr_m w_rd t_ w_rd.

How the tortoise got its shell

Read the story and answer the questions below.

The King had invited all the animals to his castle for his wedding feast. Only the tortoise stayed away, and the King did not understand why. So the next day he asked the tortoise why it had not joined the other animals at the feast. "There's no place like home," the tortoise replied. This answer made the King so angry that he insisted that the tortoise carry its house on its back!

Many people would rather live a simple life in the comfort of their own home than live extravagantly in somebody else's.

1. **What was the King celebrating?**

   _____

2. **Which animal did not join the celebration?**

   _____

3. **What did the King make the tortoise do?**

   _____

4. **Which of the following describes this piece of writing?**
   a. **a poem**   b. **a fable**   c. **a nursery rhyme**

5. **Look at the last sentence in the passage. This is the moral of the story. What is a moral?**
   a. **a song**   b. **a lesson**   c. **an introduction**

Panto poster

Look at the information in the box. Write it in the correct order on the poster.

School Hall, Children £1, 7:30 p.m., Saturday 21 December,
Puss in Boots, Adults £1.50, Blithely Primary School presents

The Grand Old Duke of York

Put the rhyme in the correct order by numbering the boxes from 1 to 4.

He marched them up to the
top of the hill,
And he marched them down again.

And when they were up they were up,
And when they were down,
they were down,

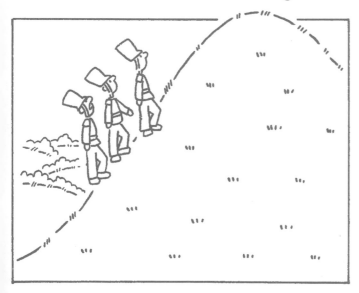

And when they were only halfway up,
They were neither up nor down.

Oh, the grand old Duke of York,
He had ten thousand men;

Down under wordsearch

Look in the wordsearch grid for six things you might find in Australia.
You will find them by reading across or down.
Circle the words as you find them.

K	A	N	G	A	R	O	O	D	U
B	O	S	E	V	L	X	N	U	B
O	X	M	I	F	Z	E	E	N	W
O	D	E	P	H	K	C	H	O	A
M	O	W	O	M	B	A	T	I	L
E	L	A	S	I	D	N	Z	R	L
R	O	D	S	O	K	O	A	L	A
A	I	T	U	N	Q	R	C	H	B
N	E	E	M	C	F	D	Q	R	Y
G	A	W	S	U	V	X	N	L	T

Alphabet names

Think of a name for a boy or girl that begins
with each letter of the alphabet.

A ppell

B eennaner

C ar

D og

E ge

F rog

G ope

H uje

I glue

J ugie

K angroy

L oug

M um

N

O

P

Q

R

S orrya

T iago

U

V an

W y

X ray

Y

Z oo

On the shelf

Encyclopedias are information books that are usually arranged in alphabetical order. Look at these encyclopedias and write which book you would look in for the subjects below. The first one has been done for you.

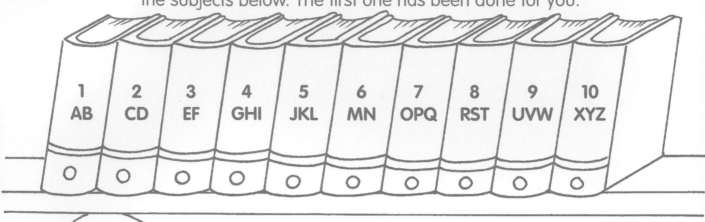

#	AB	CD	EF	GHI	JKL	MN	OPQ	RST	UVW	XYZ
1	2	3	4	4	5	6	7	8	9	10

- **1** antelopes
- [ ] fishing
- [ ] juggling
- [ ] Napoleon
- [ ] yaks
- [ ] volcanoes
- [ ] the Romans
- [ ] pirates
- [ ] windmills
- [ ] dragons
- [ ] King Henry VIII

Tense time

The **past** tense tells us what has already happened. The **present** tense tells us about something that is happening. The **future** tense tells us about something that is going to happen. In which tense are these sentences written?

1. **Farmer Green grows potatoes in his fields.**

past/present/future

2. **Carl the crow ate all the seeds.**

past/present/future

3. **When we get a scarecrow it will help scare the birds.**

past/present/future

4. **There are lots of rabbits in the fields.**

past/present/future

5. **The rabbits dug lots of burrows.**

past/present/future

6. **The gate to the field is closed.**

past/present/future

7. **Farmer Green will plant more seeds in the morning.**

past/present/future

8. **Farmer Green's tractor is red.**

past/present/future

What's it all about?

Look at the titles of these books. The contents and chapter headings are written next to each one. Look at the questions in the box. Write your answers on the lines.

How Things Work

Contents
Safety First
Wheels at Work
Rocket Power
Electrifying Activity
Glossary and Index

The Midnight Fox

Chapters
Bad News
Abandoned
Discovery at the Field
The Search
Unwilling Hunter
Captured
A Memory

The Complete Book of Gardening

Contents
Designing your Garden
The Fruit and Vegetable Garden
Decorative Garden Plants
Gardening Techniques
Glossary and Index

A Journey Through Time

Contents
Time Chart
Early Man
The Greeks
The Romans
The Vikings
Index

Mountains and Valleys

Contents
The Changing World
The Restless Earth
Mountain Plants
Mountain Creatures
Valley Dwellers
Glossary and Index

1. Which book is about history? . . . .

2. Which book is about science? . . . .

3. Which book tells you how to grow tomatoes? . . . .

4. Which book is fiction? . . . .

5. All the other books are non-fiction. What do they have in common? . . . .

. . . .

. . . .

Jock Jackdaw's punctuation

Mischievous Jock Jackdaw has stolen some of the punctuation and capital letters from this story. Can you see what is missing?

The Magic Porridge Pot

Once upon a time there was a little girl who lived with her mother. they were very poor and had nothing to eat One day the girl met an old woman who gave her a little pot. All she had to say was, "cook, little pot, cook, and the pot would cook good, sweet porridge. to make it stop cooking she just had to say "Stop, little pot, stop"

one day when the girl went for a walk, the mother felt hungry and asked the pot to cook But she did not know how to stop it and soon the porridge began to cover the kitchen and then the house it was not long before all the houses in the street were full of porridge

Just as the porridge was reaching the last house in town, the little girl came home and said, Stop, little pot, stop from that day on anyone who wanted to come back to the town had to eat their way through the porridge.

Rewrite the story in your neatest handwriting and add the punctuation and capital letters.

Barnyard crossword

The pictures are clues to these barnyard things.
Follow the numbers across and down to complete the crossword.

Rhyming balloons

Find the words that rhyme and colour the pairs the same colour.

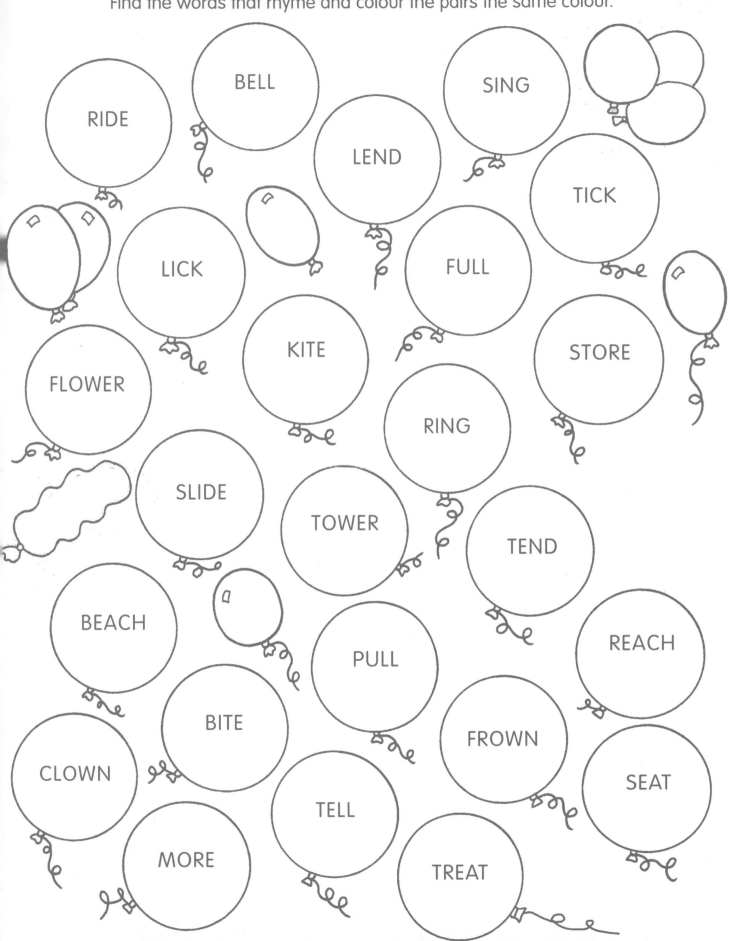

The Three Billy Goats Gruff

Read this story, then answer the questions on the next page.

Once there were three billy goats called Gruff. They lived in the mountains, searching for the fresh, green grass they loved to eat. On the other side of a river was the freshest, greenest grass they had ever seen. The goats trotted towards the river until they came to a bridge.

"The bridge may not be very strong," said the smallest goat. "I will go first to make sure it is safe." Under the bridge there lived a wicked old troll. When the smallest goat's hooves went trip, trap on the wooden planks, the troll peeped over the edge of the bridge.

"Who's that trip-trapping across my bridge? I'm a troll and I'm going to eat you for my dinner!" he roared.

But the goat replied, "I'm the smallest billy goat Gruff. My brother will be tastier than me." So the troll let the smallest goat go.

Next the middle-sized goat began to cross the bridge. When he was in the middle, the wicked old troll popped up again.

"Who's that trip-trapping across my bridge?" he roared. "I'll eat you up!" But the middle-sized goat replied, "Wait for my brother. He is much bigger!" So the greedy troll let the middle-sized goat go.

The biggest goat had seen everything that had happened and smiled to himself. His big hooves went trip, trap on the wooden planks. This time the troll jumped out and stood on the bridge.

"Who's that trip-trapping on my bridge?" he shouted. "Dinner at last!"

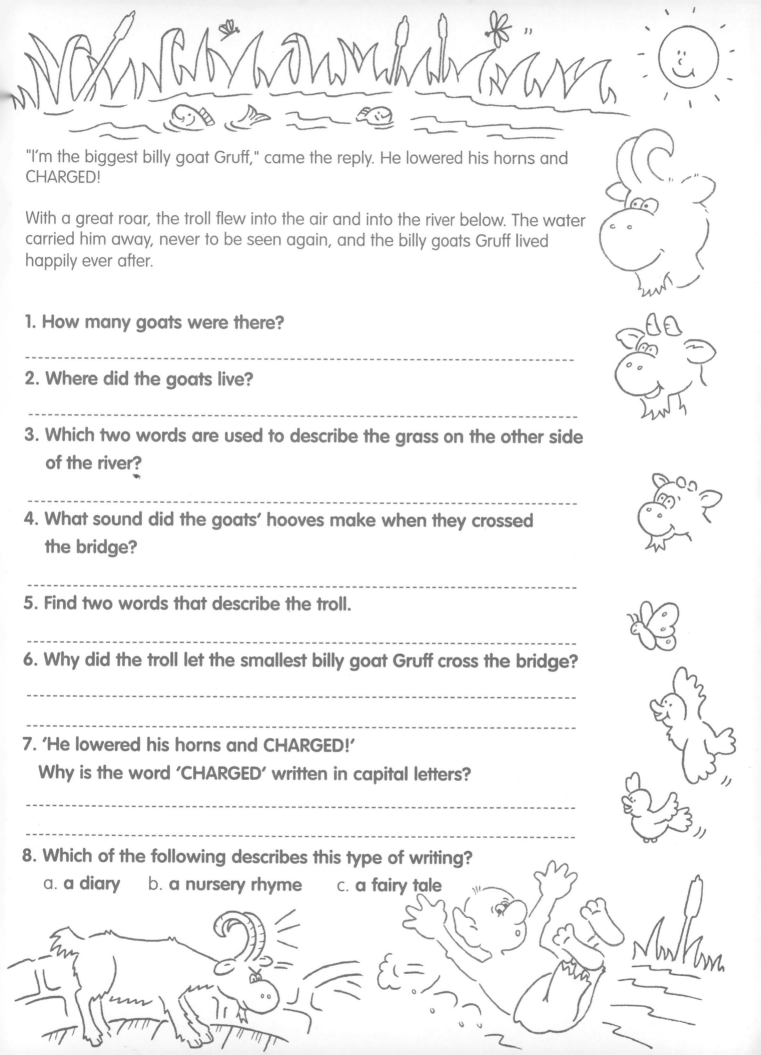

"I'm the biggest billy goat Gruff," came the reply. He lowered his horns and CHARGED!

With a great roar, the troll flew into the air and into the river below. The water carried him away, never to be seen again, and the billy goats Gruff lived happily ever after.

1. How many goats were there?

----

2. Where did the goats live?

----

3. Which two words are used to describe the grass on the other side of the river?

----

4. What sound did the goats' hooves make when they crossed the bridge?

----

5. Find two words that describe the troll.

----

6. Why did the troll let the smallest billy goat Gruff cross the bridge?

----

7. 'He lowered his horns and CHARGED!'
   Why is the word 'CHARGED' written in capital letters?

----

8. Which of the following describes this type of writing?
   a. **a diary**   b. **a nursery rhyme**   c. **a fairy tale**

Finish the poem!

Think of the best rhyming words to complete this poem.

I like spring, when the lambs come to play,
During the months of March, April and ___.

I think hot summer days are grand!
I go to the beach and dig in the ____.

I like autumn, when the winds blow free,
Shaking the leaves from every ____.

I love winter, when there's snow and a storm,
And I'm inside with Pup, all snug and ____.

Answers

Out and about
CINEMA   STAR WARS   BUTCHER   CHURCH
PARK   CITY CENTRE   BAKERY   GREENGROCER
EAST STREET   FISH & CHIPS   RESTAURANT

A sleepy surprise
1C   2D   3B   4F   5A   6E

Good spells!
wing of bat, skin of snake, whisker of kitten,
shoe of horse, toad slime, snail shell, wool of
lamb, green custard, milk of goat, mane of lion,
tail of rat, egg of ostrich, peacock feather, toe
nails, web of spider, tooth of dragon

Magic symbols
"Can you go to the store for me?" his mother
asked.
Lizzie, John and Anna took the dog for a walk.
"It was fantastic!" he yelled.
"Why does this always happen to me?" laughed
Jasmine.
The twins told their brother they were going
to be late.
"Are you travelling on this train?" Patrick asked.
"Watch out!" he shouted.
She turned the corner and ran into the house.
"Why do I have to do this?" Gwen asked.
Would she get there on time?
They grabbed their bags, coats and books.
Maria said, "I can't wait to go on holiday."
It was not long before they heard the sound again.
"Look at the snow!" cried Mark.
Frank turned and said, "You have to move
your car."

Vinnie the Vowel Muncher
Vinnie was very hungry and munched some
of the vowels in this piece of writing. He never went
to school and does not know how many vowels
there are in the alphabet. Vowels join the other
letters together. There are very few words that do
not have at least one vowel. Look at the way the
vowels behave when you read. Their sounds can
change from word to word.

How the tortoise got its shell
1. The King was celebrating his wedding.
2. The tortoise did not join the celebration.
3. The King made the tortoise carry its house
   on its back.
4. **b.** a fable
5. **b.** a lesson

The Grand Old Duke of York
1. Oh, the grand old Duke of York,
   He had ten thousand men;
2. He marched them up to the top of the hill,
   And he marched them down again.
3. And when they were up they were up,
   And when they were down, they were down,
4. And when they were only halfway up,
   They were neither up nor down.

Down under wordsearch

On the shelf
3–fishing, 5–juggling, 6–Napoleon
11–yaks, 9–volcanoes, 8–the Romans
7–pirates, 10–windmills, 2–dragons
4–King Henry VIII ('Henry' not 'King'!)

Tense time
1. present 2. past 3. future 4. present
5. past 6. present 7. future 8. present

What's it all about?
1. A Journey Through Time
2. How Things Work
3. The Complete Book of Gardening
4. The Midnight Fox
5. All of the other books are factual and
   informative. They also have a glossary
   and/or an index.

Jock Jackdaw's punctuation
The Magic Porridge Pot

Once upon a time there was a little girl who lived with her mother. They were very poor and had nothing to eat. One day the girl met an old woman who gave her a little pot. All she had to say was, "Cook, little pot, cook," and the pot would cook good, sweet porridge. To make it stop cooking she just had to say, "Stop, little pot, stop."

One day when the girl went for a walk, the mother felt hungry and asked the pot to cook. But she did not know how to stop it, and soon the porridge began to cover the kitchen and then the house. It was not long before all the houses in the street were full of porridge.

Just as the porridge was reaching the last house in town, the little girl came home and said, "Stop, little pot, stop." From that day on, anyone who wanted to come back to the town had to eat their way through the porridge.

Barnyard crossword

Rhyming balloons
RIDE–SLIDE, BELL–TELL, LEND–TEND, SING–RING, TICK–LICK, FULL–PULL , STORE–MORE, KITE–BITE, FLOWER–TOWER, REACH–BEACH, FROWN–CLOWN, SEAT–TREAT.

The Three Billy Goats Gruff
1. There were three goats.
2. They lived in the mountains.
3. The words 'fresh' and 'green' are used to describe the grass.
4. The goats' hooves made a 'trip-trapping' sound on the bridge.
5. There are three words that are used to describe the troll: 'wicked', 'old' and 'greedy'.
6. The troll was greedy and waited for the smallest goat's bigger brother to cross the bridge, because there would be more for him to eat.
7. 'CHARGED' is written in capital letters to make the word stand out and to give more emphasis.
8. **c.** a fairy tale

Finish the poem!
I like spring, when the lambs come to play,
During the months of March, April and **May**.

I think hot summer days are grand!
I go to the beach and dig in the **sand**.

I like autumn, when the winds blow free,
Shaking the leaves from every **tree**.

I love winter, when there's snow and a storm,
And I'm inside with Pup, all snug and **warm**.

Help with Homework

Adding and Subtracting

Addition tables

Learn the addition tables so you can remember them.

1 + 1 =	2
2 + 1 =	3
3 + 1 =	4
4 + 1 =	5
5 + 1 =	6
6 + 1 =	7
7 + 1 =	8
8 + 1 =	9
9 + 1 =	10
10 + 1 =	11
11 + 1 =	12
12 + 1 =	13

1 + 2 =	3
2 + 2 =	4
3 + 2 =	5
4 + 2 =	6
5 + 2 =	7
6 + 2 =	8
7 + 2 =	9
8 + 2 =	10
9 + 2 =	11
10 + 2 =	12
11 + 2 =	13
12 + 2 =	14

1 + 3 =	4
2 + 3 =	5
3 + 3 =	6
4 + 3 =	7
5 + 3 =	8
6 + 3 =	9
7 + 3 =	10
8 + 3 =	11
9 + 3 =	12
10 + 3 =	13
11 + 3 =	14
12 + 3 =	15

1 + 4 =	5
2 + 4 =	6
3 + 4 =	7
4 + 4 =	8
5 + 4 =	9
6 + 4 =	10
7 + 4 =	11
8 + 4 =	12
9 + 4 =	13
10 + 4 =	14
11 + 4 =	15
12 + 4 =	16

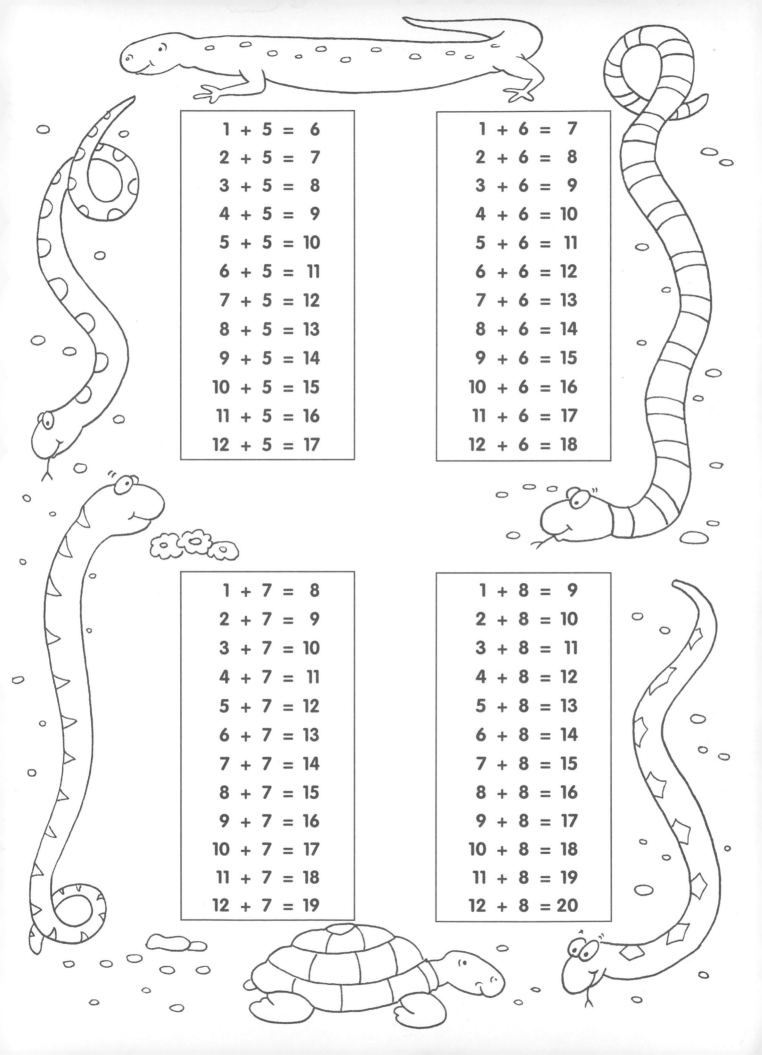

1 + 5 = 6		1 + 6 = 7
2 + 5 = 7		2 + 6 = 8
3 + 5 = 8		3 + 6 = 9
4 + 5 = 9		4 + 6 = 10
5 + 5 = 10		5 + 6 = 11
6 + 5 = 11		6 + 6 = 12
7 + 5 = 12		7 + 6 = 13
8 + 5 = 13		8 + 6 = 14
9 + 5 = 14		9 + 6 = 15
10 + 5 = 15		10 + 6 = 16
11 + 5 = 16		11 + 6 = 17
12 + 5 = 17		12 + 6 = 18

1 + 7 = 8		1 + 8 = 9
2 + 7 = 9		2 + 8 = 10
3 + 7 = 10		3 + 8 = 11
4 + 7 = 11		4 + 8 = 12
5 + 7 = 12		5 + 8 = 13
6 + 7 = 13		6 + 8 = 14
7 + 7 = 14		7 + 8 = 15
8 + 7 = 15		8 + 8 = 16
9 + 7 = 16		9 + 8 = 17
10 + 7 = 17		10 + 8 = 18
11 + 7 = 18		11 + 8 = 19
12 + 7 = 19		12 + 8 = 20

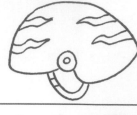
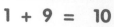

1 + 9 =	10	1 + 10 =	11
2 + 9 =	11	2 + 10 =	12
3 + 9 =	12	3 + 10 =	13
4 + 9 =	13	4 + 10 =	14
5 + 9 =	14	5 + 10 =	15
6 + 9 =	15	6 + 10 =	16
7 + 9 =	16	7 + 10 =	17
8 + 9 =	17	8 + 10 =	18
9 + 9 =	18	9 + 10 =	19
10 + 9 =	19	10 + 10 =	20
11 + 9 =	20	11 + 10 =	21
12 + 9 =	21	12 + 10 =	22

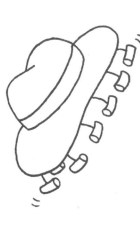

1 + 11 =	12	1 + 12 =	13
2 + 11 =	13	2 + 12 =	14
3 + 11 =	14	3 + 12 =	15
4 + 11 =	15	4 + 12 =	16
5 + 11 =	16	5 + 12 =	17
6 + 11 =	17	6 + 12 =	18
7 + 11 =	18	7 + 12 =	19
8 + 11 =	19	8 + 12 =	20
9 + 11 =	20	9 + 12 =	21
10 + 11 =	21	10 + 12 =	22
11 + 11 =	22	11 + 12 =	23
12 + 11 =	23	12 + 12 =	24

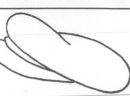

Elephant sums

Do the sums and write the answers in the buckets.

6 + 2 = 8

4 + 4 = 8

3 + 7 = 10

Addition on the farm

Complete the sums.

4 + **4** = 8

☐ + 7 = 12

7 + ☐ = 14

4 + 3 = **7**

☐ + 6 = 18

9 + ☐ = 16

11 + 5 = ☐

☐ + 8 = 20

8 + 8 = ☐

12 + ☐ = 24

☐ + 8 = 15

10 + 3 = ☐

9 + ☐ = 18

12 + ☐ = 22

11 + 3 = ☐

☐ + 6 = 13

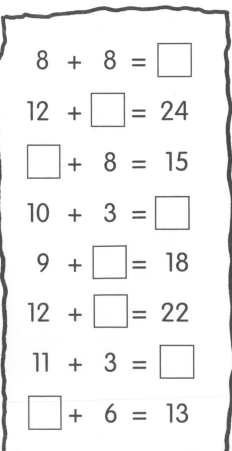

11 + 11 = ☐

7 + ☐ = 19

4 + 3 = ☐

☐ + 11 = 11

8 + ☐ = 21

20 + 3 = ☐

32 + ☐ = 35

18 + 12 = ☐

12 + 12 = ☐

1 + ☐ = 10

☐ + 10 = 20

7 + 9 = ☐

2 + ☐ = 4

8 + 2 = ☐

9 + 7 = ☐

3 + ☐ = 6

Missing numbers

Count the objects to complete the sums.

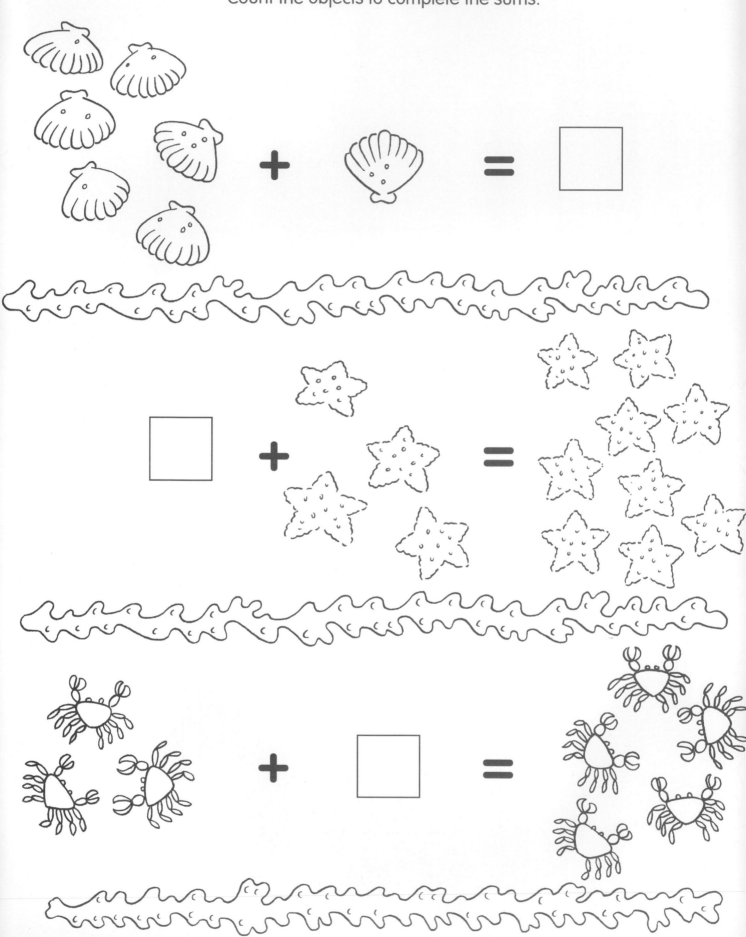

Window sums

Do the sums and write your answers on the doors.

3

+

12

=

5

+

5

=

9

+

6

=

15

10

15

Kite sums

Do the sums by counting the bows on the kites.
When you have an answer, draw the number of bows on the last kite.
The first one has been started for you.

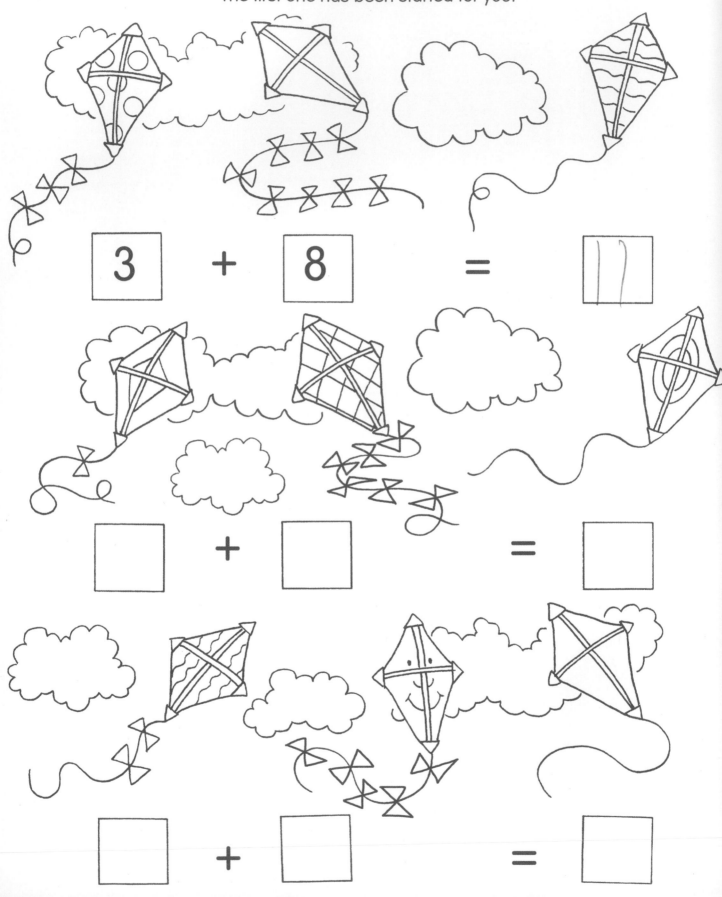

3	+	8	=	

	+		=	

	+		=	

Balloon sums

The answers to the balloon sums are printed on the children's T-shirts.
Draw a line to join each balloon to the correct child.

$8 + 11 = 19$

$9 + 9 =$

$12 + 10 = 22$

18

22

19

Sums puzzles

Do the sums in the grids by filling in the missing numbers.

	+	8	=	12
+	■	+	■	+
1	+		=	
=	■	=	■	=
	+	11	=	16

11	+		=	20
+	■	+	■	+
	+	2	=	4
=	■	=	■	=
	+	11	=	

Sums crossword

Do the sums. Follow the letters across and down, and write the answers as words in the crossword grid.

a. $6 + 6 =$ ☐

a. $2 + 0 =$ ☐

b. $3 + 7 =$ ☐

c. $9 + 2 =$ ☐

d. $3 + 1 =$ ☐

e. $1 + 0 =$ ☐

f. $2 + 1 =$ ☐

g. $5 + 3 =$ ☐

Number lines

Do the sums in the hot-air balloons.
Draw lines to join each answer to its place on the number line.

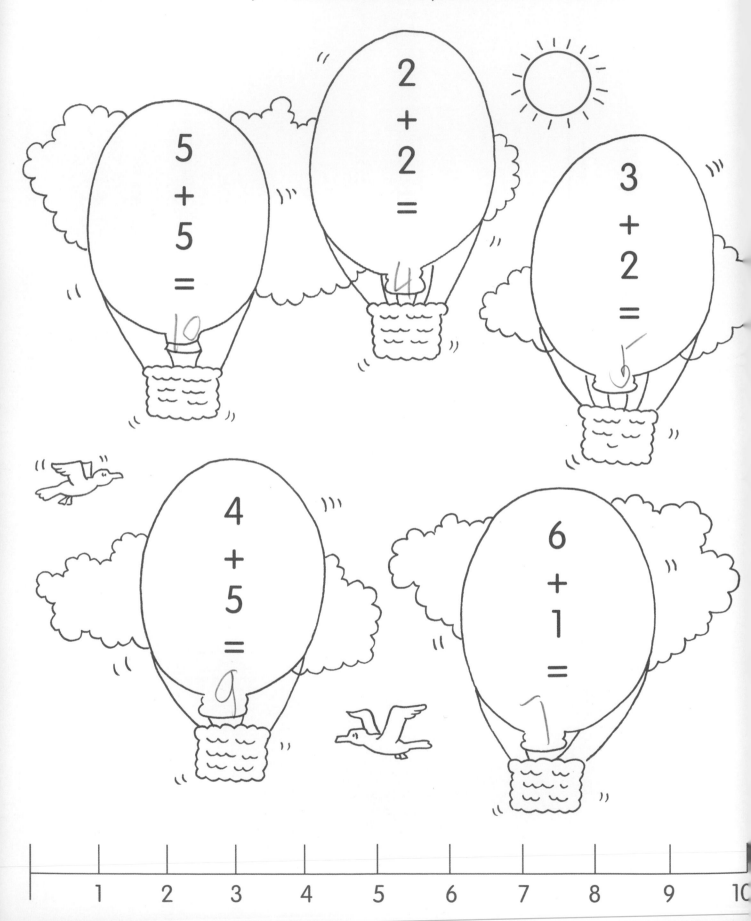

1   2   3   4   5   6   7   8   9   10

Match the answers

Draw lines to join the sums on the sailboats to their answers on the anchors.

7 + 7 =

8 + 8 = 16

11 + 11 =

10 + 10 = 20

16   20   14   22

Addition test

Do the sums and write the answers in the boxes.
Check your answers by looking at the tables.

11 + 2 = 13 ✓

6 + 7 = 13 ✓

10 + 5 = 15 ✓

6 + 9 = 15 ✓

3 + 12 = 15 ✓

2 + 8 = 10 ✓

7 + 6 = 13 ✓

5 + 5 = 10 ✓

8 + 8 = 14 ✗

10 + 3 = 13 ✓

2 + 2 = 4 ✓

4 + 5 = 9 ✓

5 + 8 = 12 ✗

1	+ 9	=	10
3	+ 3	=	6
6	+ 6	=	12
4	+ 7	=	11
9	+ 6	=	13
11	+ 11	=	22
7	+ 12	=	19
3	+ 9	=	12
4	+ 2	=	6
12	+ 4	=	16
8	+ 4	=	12
10	+ 6	=	16
5	+ 3	=	8

Subtraction tables

Learn the subtraction tables so you can remember them.

2 - 1 = 1	3 - 2 = 1
3 - 1 = 2	4 - 2 = 2
4 - 1 = 3	5 - 2 = 3
5 - 1 = 4	6 - 2 = 4
6 - 1 = 5	7 - 2 = 5
7 - 1 = 6	8 - 2 = 6
8 - 1 = 7	9 - 2 = 7
9 - 1 = 8	10 - 2 = 8
10 - 1 = 9	11 - 2 = 9
11 - 1 = 10	12 - 2 = 10
12 - 1 = 11	13 - 2 = 11
13 - 1 = 12	14 - 2 = 12

4 - 3 = 1	5 - 4 = 1
5 - 3 = 2	6 - 4 = 2
6 - 3 = 3	7 - 4 = 3
7 - 3 = 4	8 - 4 = 4
8 - 3 = 5	9 - 4 = 5
9 - 3 = 6	10 - 4 = 6
10 - 3 = 7	11 - 4 = 7
11 - 3 = 8	12 - 4 = 8
12 - 3 = 9	13 - 4 = 9
13 - 3 = 10	14 - 4 = 10
14 - 3 = 11	15 - 4 = 11
15 - 3 = 12	16 - 4 = 12

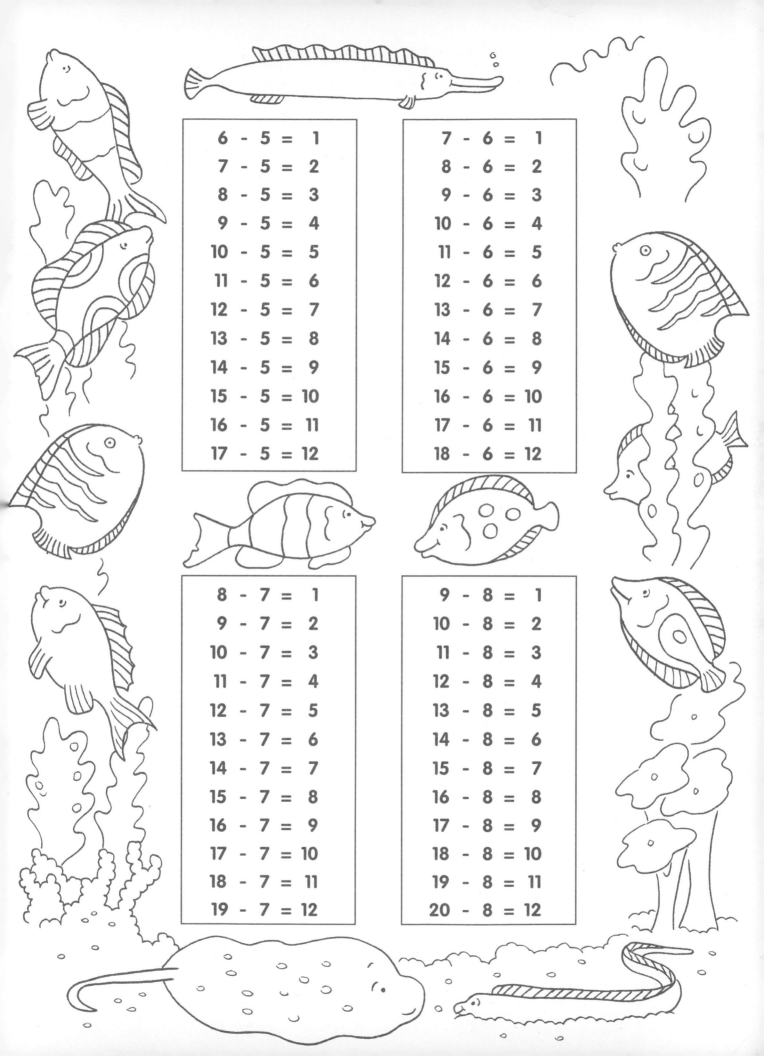

6	-	5	=	1
7	-	5	=	2
8	-	5	=	3
9	-	5	=	4
10	-	5	=	5
11	-	5	=	6
12	-	5	=	7
13	-	5	=	8
14	-	5	=	9
15	-	5	=	10
16	-	5	=	11
17	-	5	=	12

7	-	6	=	1
8	-	6	=	2
9	-	6	=	3
10	-	6	=	4
11	-	6	=	5
12	-	6	=	6
13	-	6	=	7
14	-	6	=	8
15	-	6	=	9
16	-	6	=	10
17	-	6	=	11
18	-	6	=	12

8	-	7	=	1
9	-	7	=	2
10	-	7	=	3
11	-	7	=	4
12	-	7	=	5
13	-	7	=	6
14	-	7	=	7
15	-	7	=	8
16	-	7	=	9
17	-	7	=	10
18	-	7	=	11
19	-	7	=	12

9	-	8	=	1
10	-	8	=	2
11	-	8	=	3
12	-	8	=	4
13	-	8	=	5
14	-	8	=	6
15	-	8	=	7
16	-	8	=	8
17	-	8	=	9
18	-	8	=	10
19	-	8	=	11
20	-	8	=	12

10	- 9 =	1
11	- 9 =	2
12	- 9 =	3
13	- 9 =	4
14	- 9 =	5
15	- 9 =	6
16	- 9 =	7
17	- 9 =	8
18	- 9 =	9
19	- 9 =	10
20	- 9 =	11
21	- 9 =	12

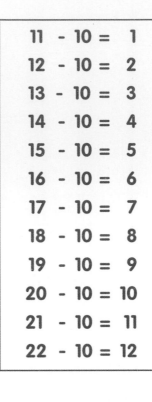

11	- 10 =	1
12	- 10 =	2
13	- 10 =	3
14	- 10 =	4
15	- 10 =	5
16	- 10 =	6
17	- 10 =	7
18	- 10 =	8
19	- 10 =	9
20	- 10 =	10
21	- 10 =	11
22	- 10 =	12

12	- 11 =	1
13	- 11 =	2
14	- 11 =	3
15	- 11 =	4
16	- 11 =	5
17	- 11 =	6
18	- 11 =	7
19	- 11 =	8
20	- 11 =	9
21	- 11 =	10
22	- 11 =	11
23	- 11 =	12

13	- 12 =	1
14	- 12 =	2
15	- 12 =	3
16	- 12 =	4
17	- 12 =	5
18	- 12 =	6
19	- 12 =	7
20	- 12 =	8
21	- 12 =	9
22	- 12 =	10
23	- 12 =	11
24	- 12 =	12

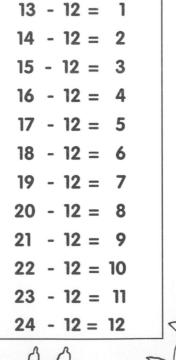

Penguin sums

Do the sums.

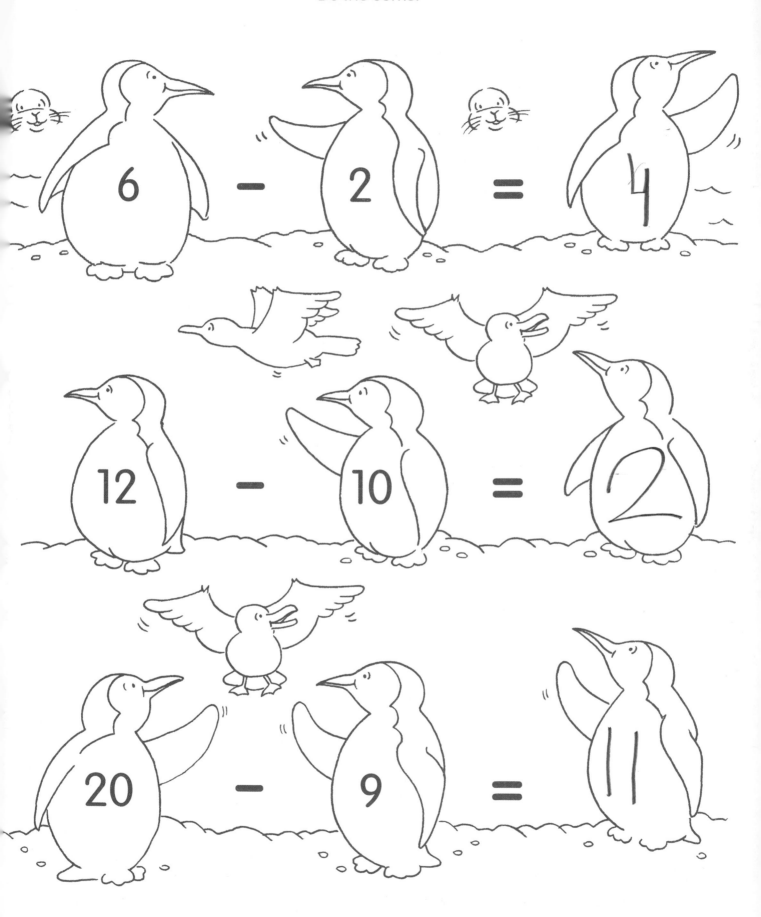

6 − 2 = 4

12 − 10 = 2

20 − 9 = 11

Subtraction in space

Complete the sums.

3 − □ = 0

□ − 4 = 8

21 − □ = 14

15 − 5 = □

□ − 6 = 18

14 − □ = 12

9 − 1 = □

□ − 2 = 16

16 − 7 = □

24 − □ = 24

□ − 9 = 0

18 − 10 = □

22 − □ = 11

9 − □ = 8

12 − 4 = □

□ − 7 = 15

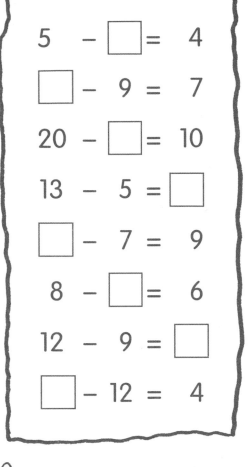

$5 - \boxed{} = 4$

$\boxed{} - 9 = 7$

$20 - \boxed{} = 10$

$13 - 5 = \boxed{}$

$\boxed{} - 7 = 9$

$8 - \boxed{} = 6$

$12 - 9 = \boxed{}$

$\boxed{} - 12 = 4$

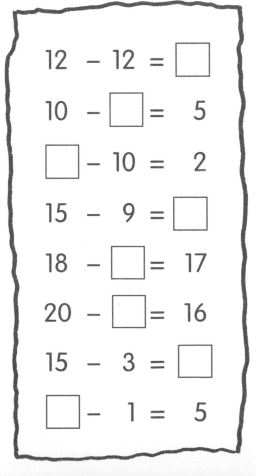

$12 - 12 = \boxed{}$

$10 - \boxed{} = 5$

$\boxed{} - 10 = 2$

$15 - 9 = \boxed{}$

$18 - \boxed{} = 17$

$20 - \boxed{} = 16$

$15 - 3 = \boxed{}$

$\boxed{} - 1 = 5$

Bubble sums

Working upwards from the bubbles on the bottom, do the sums by filling in the missing numbers.

Fun with sums

Solve these problems.

Take 4 bananas away from these monkeys.
How many bananas are left?

6

If 3 parrots fly away, how many parrots are left?

7

Colour 6 of the crocodile's teeth. How many teeth are left white?

1

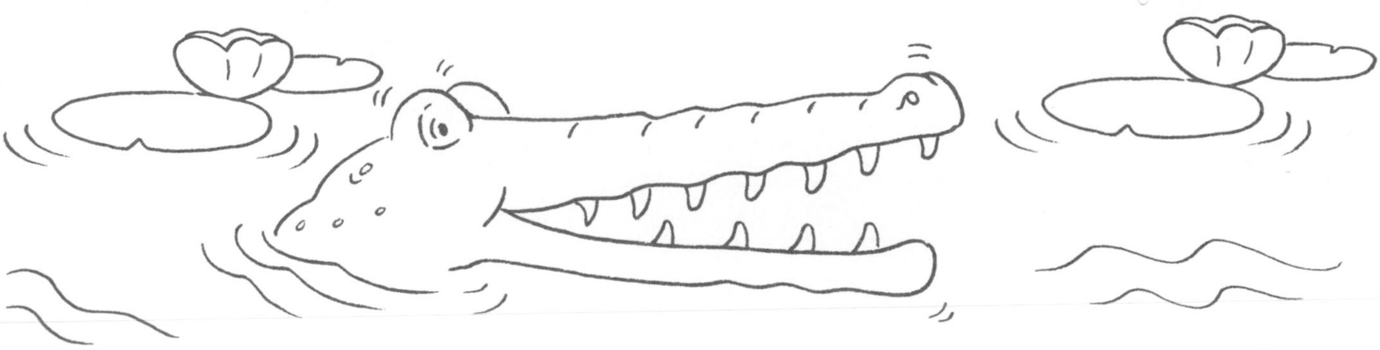

Two rabbits eat 2 carrots each.
How many carrots are left?

6

Draw 8 lighted candles on this cake.
If the boy blows out 3 candles,
how many lighted candles are left?

6

Which is right?

Circle the sums with answers that match
the numbers at the top of each box.

18
10 − 7
33 − 12
15 − 3
27 − 9

40
25 − 5
50 − 10
48 − 6
10 − 5

24
30 − 6
42 − 7
64 − 8
20 − 2

21
45 − 5
21 − 7
30 − 9
10 − 4

10
5 − 5
10 − 1
12 − 2
18 − 7

8
88 − 10
16 − 8
12 − 6
72 − 9

Taking away wordsearch

Do the sums and write the answers in the boxes.
Look for the written answers in the wordsearch grid.
You will find them by reading across and down.
Draw a ring around the words as you find them.

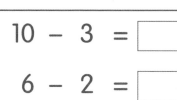

10 – 3 = ☐	15 – 9 = ☐
6 – 2 = ☐	20 – 10 = ☐
12 – 7 = ☐	50 – 20 = ☐
3 – 2 = ☐	8 – 6 = ☐

```
I   E   R   F   O   R   T   B   N
X   K   S   P   S   O   H   J   H
A   S   E   P   C   D   I   V   G
F   I   V   E   Y   T   R   E   X
B   N   E   W   E   R   T   E   N
H   B   N   E   M   K   Y   O   P
T   I   J   F   Y   A   G   S   X
W   D   F   O   N   E   B   I   J
O   Y   T   U   E   X   R   X   N
M   A   I   R   B   F   G   R   E
```

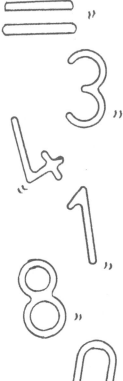

Subtraction test

Do the sums and write the answers in the boxes.
Check your answers by looking at the tables.

8   –   4   = ☐

12   –   2   = ☐

17   –   5   = ☐

20   –   9   = ☐

9   –   1   = ☐

13   –   5   = ☐

24   –   12   = ☐

5   –   5   = ☐

11   –   3   = ☐

20   –   12   = ☐

10   –   4   = ☐

23   –   11   = ☐

13 − 8 = ☐

11 − 1 = ☐

15 − 9 = ☐

3 − 3 = ☐

18 − 6 = ☐

7 − 2 = ☐

16 − 6 = ☐

15 − 5 = ☐

17 − 3 = ☐

7 − 3 = ☐

14 − 12 = ☐

17 − 8 = ☐

6 − 5 = ☐

22 − 10 = ☐

Answers

Elephant sums
6 + 2 = 8   4 + 4 = 8   3 + 7 = 10

Addition on the farm
4 + 4 = 8   8 + 8 = 16
5 + 7 = 12   12 + 12 = 24
7 + 7 = 14   7 + 8 = 15
4 + 3 = 7   10 + 3 = 13
12 + 6 = 18   9 + 9 = 18
9 + 7 = 16   12 + 10 = 22
11 + 5 = 16   11 + 3 = 14
12 + 8 = 20   7 + 6 = 13

11 + 11 = 22   12 + 12 = 24
7 + 12 = 19   1 + 9 = 10
4 + 3 = 7   10 + 10 = 20
0 + 11 = 11   7 + 9 = 16
8 + 13 = 21   2 + 2 = 4
20 + 3 = 23   8 + 2 = 10
32 + 3 = 35   9 + 7 = 16
18 + 12 = 30   3 + 3 = 6

Missing numbers
6 + 1 = 7   5 + 4 = 9   3 + 2 = 5

Window sums
3 + 12 = 15   5 + 5 = 10   9 + 6 = 15

Kite sums
3 + 8 = 11   1 + 6 = 7   2 + 5 = 7

Balloon sums
8 + 11 = 19   9 + 9 = 18   12 + 10 = 22

Sums puzzles

4	+	8	=	12
+		+		+
1	+	3	=	4
=		=		=
5	+	11	=	16

11	+	9	=	20
+		+		+
2	+	2	=	4
=		=		=
13	+	11	=	24

Sums crossword
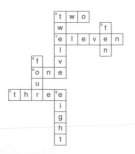

Number lines
5 + 5 = 10   2 + 2 = 4   3 + 2 = 5
4 + 5 = 9   6 + 1 = 7

Match the answers
7 + 7 = 14   8 + 8 = 16
11 + 11 = 22   10 + 10 = 20

Penguin sums
6 - 2 = 4   12 - 10 = 2   20 - 9 = 11

Subtractions in space
3 − 3 = 0   16 − 7 = 9
12 − 4 = 8   24 − 0 = 24
21 − 7 = 14   9 − 9 = 0
15 − 5 = 10   18 − 10 = 8
24 − 6 = 18   22 − 11 = 11
14 − 2 = 12   9 − 1 = 8
9 − 1 = 8   12 − 4 = 8
18 − 2 = 16   22 − 7 = 15

5 − 1 = 4   12 − 12 = 0
16 − 9 = 7   10 − 5 = 5
20 − 10 = 10   12 − 10 = 2
13 − 5 = 8   15 − 9 = 6
16 − 7 = 9   18 − 1 = 17
8 − 2 = 6   20 − 4 = 16
12 − 9 = 3   15 − 3 = 12
16 − 12 = 4   6 − 1 = 5

Bubble sums
10 - 5 = 5   12 - 7 = 5   8 - 3 = 5
12 - 5 = 7   12 - 3 = 9   14 - 5 = 9

Fun with sums
2 bananas are left   2 carrots are left
4 parrots are left   5 candles are left
5 teeth are left white

Which is right?
27 - 9 = 18   50 - 10 = 40   30 - 6 = 24
30 - 9 = 21   12 - 2 = 10   16 - 8 = 16

Taking away wordsearch

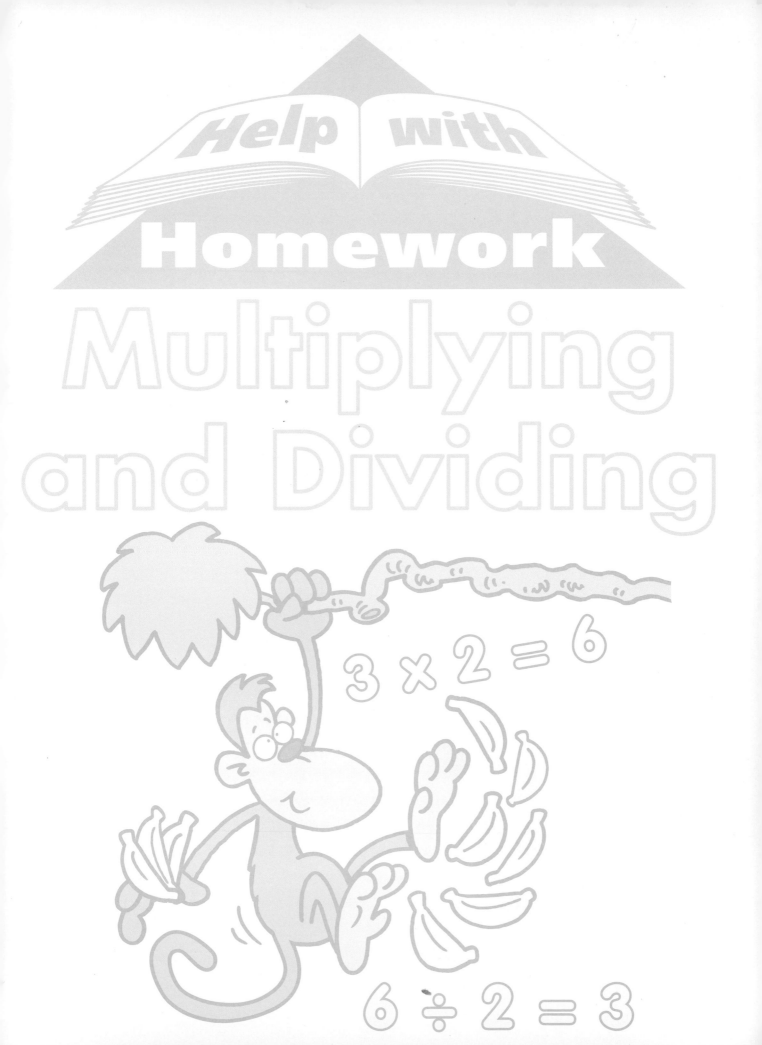

Multiplication tables

Learn the multiplication tables so you can remember them.

1 x 1	=	1
2 x 1	=	2
3 x 1	=	3
4 x 1	=	4
5 x 1	=	5
6 x 1	=	6
7 x 1	=	7
8 x 1	=	8
9 x 1	=	9
10 x 1	=	10
11 x 1	=	11
12 x 1	=	12

1 x 2	=	2
2 x 2	=	4
3 x 2	=	6
4 x 2	=	8
5 x 2	=	10
6 x 2	=	12
7 x 2	=	14
8 x 2	=	16
9 x 2	=	18
10 x 2	=	20
11 x 2	=	22
12 x 2	=	24

1 x 3	=	3
2 x 3	=	6
3 x 3	=	9
4 x 3	=	12
5 x 3	=	15
6 x 3	=	18
7 x 3	=	21
8 x 3	=	24
9 x 3	=	27
10 x 3	=	30
11 x 3	=	33
12 x 3	=	36

1 x 4	=	4
2 x 4	=	8
3 x 4	=	12
4 x 4	=	16
5 x 4	=	20
6 x 4	=	24
7 x 4	=	28
8 x 4	=	32
9 x 4	=	36
10 x 4	=	40
11 x 4	=	44
12 x 4	=	48

1 x 5 = 5	1 x 6 = 6
2 x 5 = 10	2 x 6 = 12
3 x 5 = 15	3 x 6 = 18
4 x 5 = 20	4 x 6 = 24
5 x 5 = 25	5 x 6 = 30
6 x 5 = 30	6 x 6 = 36
7 x 5 = 35	7 x 6 = 42
8 x 5 = 40	8 x 6 = 48
9 x 5 = 45	9 x 6 = 54
10 x 5 = 50	10 x 6 = 60
11 x 5 = 55	11 x 6 = 66
12 x 5 = 60	12 x 6 = 72

1 x 7 = 7	1 x 8 = 8
2 x 7 = 14	2 x 8 = 16
3 x 7 = 21	3 x 8 = 24
4 x 7 = 28	4 x 8 = 32
5 x 7 = 35	5 x 8 = 40
6 x 7 = 42	6 x 8 = 48
7 x 7 = 49	7 x 8 = 56
8 x 7 = 56	8 x 8 = 64
9 x 7 = 63	9 x 8 = 72
10 x 7 = 70	10 x 8 = 80
11 x 7 = 77	11 x 8 = 88
12 x 7 = 84	12 x 8 = 96

1 x 9 = 9		1 x 10 = 10
2 x 9 = 18		2 x 10 = 20
3 x 9 = 27		3 x 10 = 30
4 x 9 = 36		4 x 10 = 40
5 x 9 = 45		5 x 10 = 50
6 x 9 = 54		6 x 10 = 60
7 x 9 = 63		7 x 10 = 70
8 x 9 = 72		8 x 10 = 80
9 x 9 = 81		9 x 10 = 90
10 x 9 = 90		10 x 10 = 100
11 x 9 = 99		11 x 10 = 110
12 x 9 = 108		12 x 10 = 120

1 x 11 = 11		1 x 12 = 12
2 x 11 = 22		2 x 12 = 24
3 x 11 = 33		3 x 12 = 36
4 x 11 = 44		4 x 12 = 48
5 x 11 = 55		5 x 12 = 60
6 x 11 = 66		6 x 12 = 72
7 x 11 = 77		7 x 12 = 84
8 x 11 = 88		8 x 12 = 96
9 x 11 = 99		9 x 12 = 108
10 x 11 = 110		10 x 12 = 120
11 x 11 = 121		11 x 12 = 132
12 x 11 = 132		12 x 12 = 144

Multiplication sums

Do the sums and write the answers on the rocks.

3 x 8 =

5 x 6 =

7 x 2 =

Missing numbers

Complete the multiplication sums.

$2 \times \boxed{} = 4$

$\boxed{} \times 5 = 15$

$7 \times \boxed{} = 14$

$3 \times 3 = \boxed{}$

$\boxed{} \times 5 = 30$

$9 \times \boxed{} = 18$

$4 \times 5 = \boxed{}$

$\boxed{} \times 3 = 3$

$4 \times 4 = \boxed{}$

$7 \times \boxed{} = 56$

$\boxed{} \times 4 = 8$

$11 \times 3 = \boxed{}$

$9 \times \boxed{} = 45$

$6 \times \boxed{} = 36$

$8 \times 3 = \boxed{}$

$\boxed{} \times 7 = 28$

$12 \times 5 = \boxed{}$

$10 \times \boxed{} = 30$

$4 \times 3 = \boxed{}$

$\boxed{} \times 11 = 11$

$8 \times \boxed{} = 40$

$9 \times 3 = \boxed{}$

$8 \times \boxed{} = 72$

$12 \times 12 = \boxed{}$

$11 \times 10 = \boxed{}$

$6 \times \boxed{} = 48$

$\boxed{} \times 4 = 24$

$7 \times 9 = \boxed{}$

$2 \times \boxed{} = 4$

$12 \times 8 = \boxed{}$

$9 \times 9 = \boxed{}$

$3 \times \boxed{} = 21$

Missing bees

Draw more bees to complete the sums.

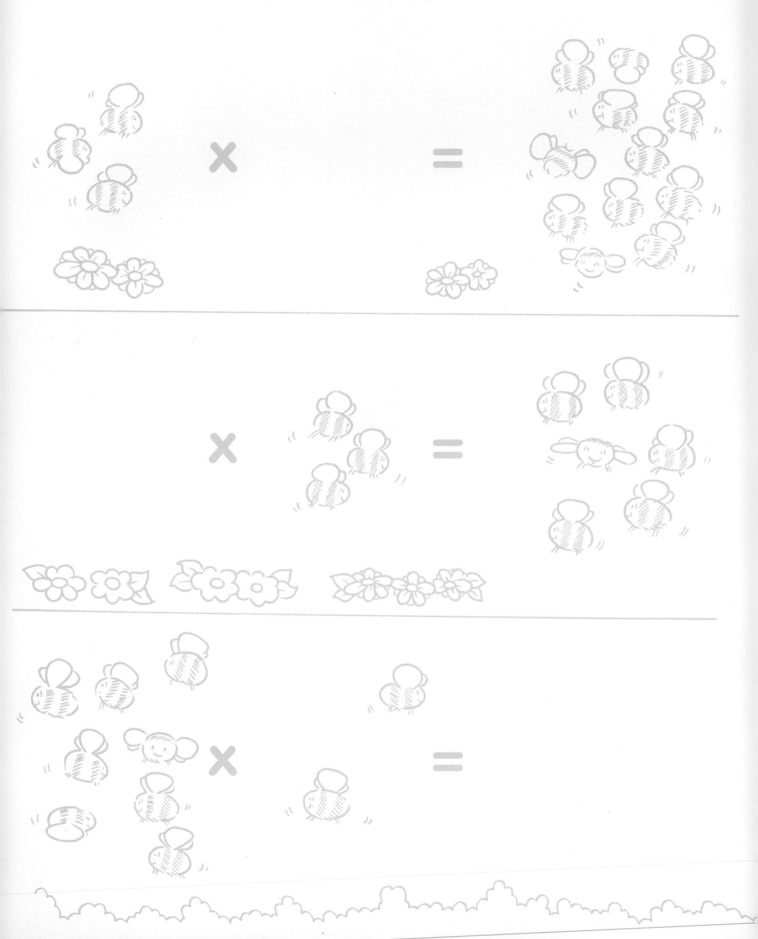

Sum ladders

Do the sums in the ladders and write the answers on the buckets.

Flower sums

Count the petals and write the number in the centre of each flower.
Then do the sums. You could draw the missing petals on the last flower in each row.
Look at the example to help you.

Example:

Magical numbers

The children are holding the answers to the sums on the cooking pots.
Draw a line to join each child to the correct pot.

Sums puzzles

Do the sums in the grids by filling in the missing numbers.

Sums crossword

Do the sums. Following the letters across and down, write the answers
as words in the crossword grid.

a. $3 \times 4 =$ ☐

b. $2 \times 1 =$ ☐

c. $2 \times 7 =$ ☐

c. $5 \times 10 =$ ☐

d. $3 \times 3 =$ ☐

e. $1 \times 11 =$ ☐

f. $7 \times 10 =$ ☐

g. $10 \times 1 =$ ☐

Match the answers

Do the sums on the spaceships. Look at the answers then draw
a line to join the correct aliens to the spaceships.

Multiplication test

Do the sums and write the answers in the boxes.
Check your answers by looking at the tables.

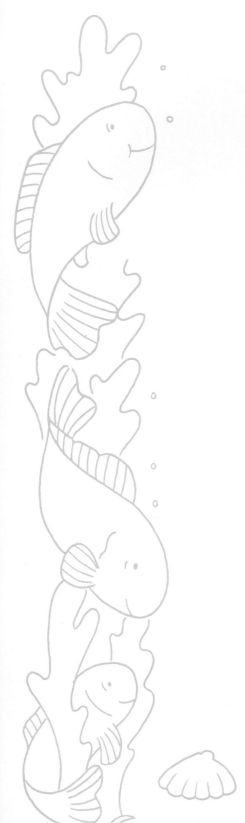

2 × 2 =

4 × 5 =

8 × 8 =

1 × 3 =

5 × 8 =

6 × 7 =

11 × 2 =

10 × 10 =

6 × 9 =

3 × 12 =

2 × 8 =

7 × 6 =

5 × 5 =

7 × 12 =

3 × 9 =

4 × 4 =

5 × 4 =

4 × 7 =

9 × 6 =

11 × 11 =

8 × 4 =

12 × 6 =

1 × 9 =

3 × 3 =

6 × 6 =

8 × 3 =

Division tables

Learn the division tables so you can remember them.

1 ÷ 1 =	1
2 ÷ 1 =	2
3 ÷ 1 =	3
4 ÷ 1 =	4
5 ÷ 1 =	5
6 ÷ 1 =	6
7 ÷ 1 =	7
8 ÷ 1 =	8
9 ÷ 1 =	9
10 ÷ 1 =	10
11 ÷ 1 =	11
12 ÷ 1 =	12

2 ÷ 2 =	1
4 ÷ 2 =	2
6 ÷ 2 =	3
8 ÷ 2 =	4
10 ÷ 2 =	5
12 ÷ 2 =	6
14 ÷ 2 =	7
16 ÷ 2 =	8
18 ÷ 2 =	9
20 ÷ 2 =	10
22 ÷ 2 =	11
24 ÷ 2 =	12

3 ÷ 3 =	1
6 ÷ 3 =	2
9 ÷ 3 =	3
12 ÷ 3 =	4
15 ÷ 3 =	5
18 ÷ 3 =	6
21 ÷ 3 =	7
24 ÷ 3 =	8
27 ÷ 3 =	9
30 ÷ 3 =	10
33 ÷ 3 =	11
36 ÷ 3 =	12

4 ÷ 4 =	1
8 ÷ 4 =	2
12 ÷ 4 =	3
16 ÷ 4 =	4
20 ÷ 4 =	5
24 ÷ 4 =	6
28 ÷ 4 =	7
32 ÷ 4 =	8
36 ÷ 4 =	9
40 ÷ 4 =	10
44 ÷ 4 =	11
48 ÷ 4 =	12

5 ÷ 5 = 1		6 ÷ 6 = 1
10 ÷ 5 = 2		12 ÷ 6 = 2
15 ÷ 5 = 3		18 ÷ 6 = 3
20 ÷ 5 = 4		24 ÷ 6 = 4
25 ÷ 5 = 5		30 ÷ 6 = 5
30 ÷ 5 = 6		36 ÷ 6 = 6
35 ÷ 5 = 7		42 ÷ 6 = 7
40 ÷ 5 = 8		48 ÷ 6 = 8
45 ÷ 5 = 9		54 ÷ 6 = 9
50 ÷ 5 = 10		60 ÷ 6 = 10
55 ÷ 5 = 11		66 ÷ 6 = 11
60 ÷ 5 = 12		72 ÷ 6 = 12

7 ÷ 7 = 1		8 ÷ 8 = 1
14 ÷ 7 = 2		16 ÷ 8 = 2
21 ÷ 7 = 3		24 ÷ 8 = 3
28 ÷ 7 = 4		32 ÷ 8 = 4
35 ÷ 7 = 5		40 ÷ 8 = 5
42 ÷ 7 = 6		48 ÷ 8 = 6
49 ÷ 7 = 7		56 ÷ 8 = 7
56 ÷ 7 = 8		64 ÷ 8 = 8
63 ÷ 7 = 9		72 ÷ 8 = 9
70 ÷ 7 = 10		80 ÷ 8 = 10
77 ÷ 7 = 11		88 ÷ 8 = 11
84 ÷ 7 = 12		96 ÷ 8 = 12

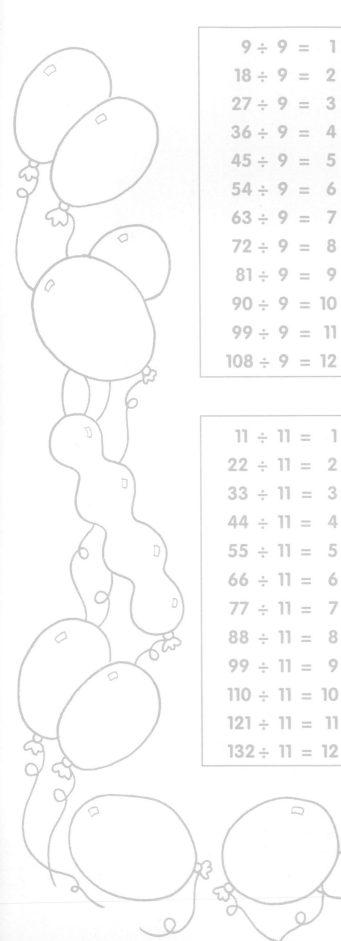

9 ÷ 9	=	1
18 ÷ 9	=	2
27 ÷ 9	=	3
36 ÷ 9	=	4
45 ÷ 9	=	5
54 ÷ 9	=	6
63 ÷ 9	=	7
72 ÷ 9	=	8
81 ÷ 9	=	9
90 ÷ 9	=	10
99 ÷ 9	=	11
108 ÷ 9	=	12

10 ÷ 10	=	1
20 ÷ 10	=	2
30 ÷ 10	=	3
40 ÷ 10	=	4
50 ÷ 10	=	5
60 ÷ 10	=	6
70 ÷ 10	=	7
80 ÷ 10	=	8
90 ÷ 10	=	9
100 ÷ 10	=	10
110 ÷ 10	=	11
120 ÷ 10	=	12

11 ÷ 11	=	1
22 ÷ 11	=	2
33 ÷ 11	=	3
44 ÷ 11	=	4
55 ÷ 11	=	5
66 ÷ 11	=	6
77 ÷ 11	=	7
88 ÷ 11	=	8
99 ÷ 11	=	9
110 ÷ 11	=	10
121 ÷ 11	=	11
132 ÷ 11	=	12

12 ÷ 12	=	1
24 ÷ 12	=	2
36 ÷ 12	=	3
48 ÷ 12	=	4
60 ÷ 12	=	5
72 ÷ 12	=	6
84 ÷ 12	=	7
96 ÷ 12	=	8
108 ÷ 12	=	9
120 ÷ 12	=	10
132 ÷ 12	=	11
144 ÷ 12	=	12

Butterfly sums

Draw more butterflies to complete the sums.

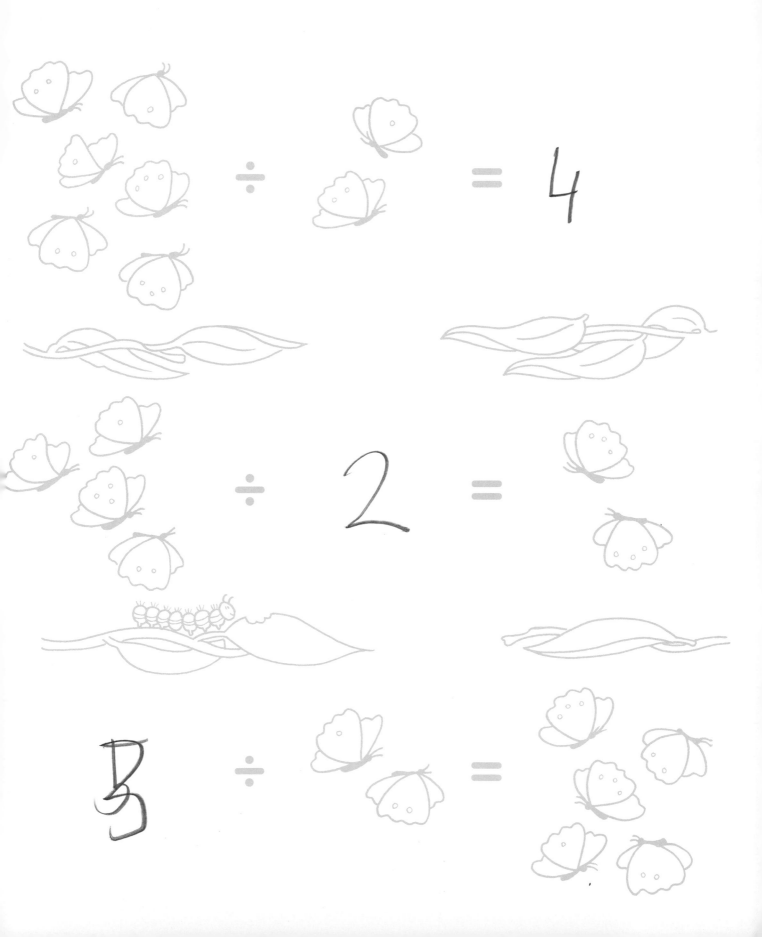

Missing numbers

Complete the sums.

$4 \div \boxed{} = 1$

$\boxed{} \div 4 = 2$

$21 \div \boxed{} = 3$

$54 \div 6 = \boxed{}$

$\boxed{} \div 6 = 6$

$63 \div \boxed{} = 7$

$49 \div 7 = \boxed{}$

$\boxed{} \div 9 = 11$

$12 \div 6 = \boxed{}$

$36 \div \boxed{} = 4$

$\boxed{} \div 9 = 1$

$56 \div 7 = \boxed{}$

$42 \div \boxed{} = 6$

$18 \div \boxed{} = 3$

$20 \div 4 = \boxed{}$

$\boxed{} \div 7 = 4$

$$24 \div \boxed{} = 4$$

$$\boxed{} \div 9 = 2$$

$$70 \div \boxed{} = 10$$

$$99 \div 9 = \boxed{}$$

$$\boxed{} \div 6 = 8$$

$$27 \div \boxed{} = 3$$

$$32 \div 4 = \boxed{}$$

$$\boxed{} \div 9 = 5$$

$$30 \div 6 = \boxed{}$$

$$10 \div \boxed{} = 2$$

$$\boxed{} \div 8 = 9$$

$$40 \div 5 = \boxed{}$$

$$90 \div \boxed{} = 9$$

$$56 \div \boxed{} = 7$$

$$6 \div 3 = \boxed{}$$

$$\boxed{} \div 8 = 3$$

Star sums

Do the sums in the stars and write the answers in the boxes.

81 ÷ 9

35 ÷ 5

49 ÷ 7

12 ÷ 6

20 ÷ 5

3 ÷ 3

32 ÷ 4

55 ÷ 11

Juggling sums

Do the sums by filling in the missing numbers.

$6 \div 3 = \boxed{}$

$\boxed{} \div 2 = 8$

$\boxed{} \div 7 = 6$

$24 \div \boxed{} = 6$

$27 \div 3 = \boxed{}$

$30 \div 5 = \boxed{}$

$9 \div \boxed{} = 9$

$\boxed{} \div 9 = 7$

Solve these problems

Share 16 books equally between 4 children.
How many books each?

Share 7 ice creams equally between 3 children. How many ice creams each?
How many left over?

Share 8 carrots equally between 2 rabbits.
How many carrots each?

Share 14 bananas equally between 7 monkeys.
How many bananas each?

Share 9 buns equally between 2 elephants. How many buns each?
How many left over?

Share 9 balloons equally between 3 clowns.
How many balloons each?

Which is right?

Circle the sums with answers that match
the numbers at the top of each box.

3	10
6 ÷ 3	12 ÷ 4
22 ÷ 2	32 ÷ 8
25 ÷ 5	60 ÷ 6
27 ÷ 9	10 ÷ 5

8	4
64 ÷ 8	36 ÷ 9
72 ÷ 12	20 ÷ 2
18 ÷ 6	16 ÷ 8
81 ÷ 9	12 ÷ 4

6	7
50 ÷ 10	88 ÷ 11
96 ÷ 12	28 ÷ 4
18 ÷ 9	12 ÷ 6
24 ÷ 4	72 ÷ 9

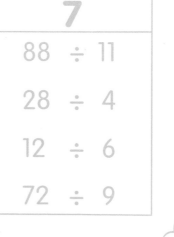

Groups

Draw rings around the following things to divide them into groups.

GROUPS OF 2

GROUPS OF 4

GROUPS OF 3

Division test

Do the sums and write the answers in the boxes.
Check your answers by looking at the tables.

$6 \div 3 =$ ☐

$14 \div 2 =$ ☐

$25 \div 5 =$ ☐

$27 \div 9 =$ ☐

$4 \div 2 =$ ☐

$64 \div 8 =$ ☐

$40 \div 4 =$ ☐

$5 \div 5 =$ ☐

$21 \div 7 =$ ☐

$8 \div 2 =$ ☐

$9 \div 1 =$ ☐

$44 \div 11 =$ ☐

20 ÷ 2 =

45 ÷ 5 =

24 ÷ 4 =

35 ÷ 7 =

18 ÷ 6 =

3 ÷ 3 =

36 ÷ 6 =

15 ÷ 5 =

70 ÷ 7 =

16 ÷ 8 =

28 ÷ 4 =

12 ÷ 3 =

56 ÷ 7 =

50 ÷ 10 =

Answers

Multiplication sums

3 × 8 = 24   5 × 6 = 30   7 × 2 = 14

Missing numbers

2 × 2 = 4   4 × 4 = 16
3 × 5 = 15   7 × 8 = 56
7 × 2 = 14   2 × 4 = 8
3 × 3 = 9   11 × 3 = 33
6 × 5 = 30   9 × 5 = 45
9 × 2 = 18   6 × 6 = 36
4 × 5 = 20   8 × 3 = 24
1 × 3 = 3   4 × 7 = 28

12 × 5 = 60   11 × 10 = 110
10 × 3 = 30   6 × 8 = 48
4 × 3 = 12   6 × 4 = 24
1 × 11 = 11   7 × 9 = 63
8 × 5 = 40   2 × 2 = 4
9 × 3 = 27   12 × 8 = 96
8 × 9 = 72   9 × 9 = 81
12 × 12 = 144 3 × 7 = 21

Missing bees

3 × 4 = 12   2 × 3 = 6   8 × 2 = 16

Sum ladders

3 × 2 = 6   5 × 5 = 25   9 × 6 = 54

Flower sums

3 × 0 = 0   3 × 4 = 12   5 × 2 = 10

Magical numbers

3 × 3 = 9   4 × 6 = 24   10 × 9 = 90

Sums puzzles

6	×	2	=	12
×		×		×
3	×	1	=	3
=		=		=
18	×	2	=	36

2	×	5	=	10
×		×		×
2	×	4	=	8
=		=		=
4	×	20	=	80

Sums crossword

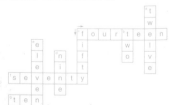

Match the answers

7 × 8 = 56   9 × 9 = 81   3 × 3 = 9
5 × 6 = 30   4 × 12 = 48   7 × 3 = 21

Butterfly sums

6 ÷ 2 = 3   4 ÷ 2 = 2   10 ÷ 2 = 5

Missing numbers

4 ÷ 4 = 1   12 ÷ 6 = 2
8 ÷ 4 = 2   36 ÷ 9 = 4
21 ÷ 7 = 3   9 ÷ 9 = 1
54 ÷ 6 = 9   56 ÷ 7 = 8
36 ÷ 6 = 6   42 ÷ 7 = 6
63 ÷ 9 = 7   18 ÷ 6 = 3
49 ÷ 7 = 7   20 ÷ 4 = 5
99 ÷ 9 = 11   28 ÷ 7 = 4

24 ÷ 6 = 4   30 ÷ 6 = 5
18 ÷ 9 = 2   10 ÷ 5 = 2
70 ÷ 7 = 10   72 ÷ 8 = 9
99 ÷ 9 = 11   40 ÷ 5 = 8
48 ÷ 6 = 8   90 ÷ 10 = 9
27 ÷ 9 = 3   56 ÷ 8 = 7
32 ÷ 4 = 8   6 ÷ 3 = 2
45 ÷ 9 = 5   24 ÷ 8 = 3

Star sums

81 ÷ 9 = 9   35 ÷ 5 = 7   49 ÷ 7 = 7
12 ÷ 6 = 2   20 ÷ 5 = 4   3 ÷ 3 = 1
32 ÷ 4 = 8   55 ÷ 11 = 5

Juggling sums

6 ÷ 3 = 2   42 ÷ 7 = 6   27 ÷ 3 = 9
9 ÷ 1 = 9   16 ÷ 2 = 8   24 ÷ 4 = 6
30 ÷ 5 = 6   63 ÷ 9 = 7

Solve these problems

Each child would have 4 books.
Each child would have 2 ice-creams.
There would be 1 left over.
Each rabbit would have 4 carrots.
Each monkey would have 2 bananas.
Each elephant would have 4 buns.
There would be 1 left over.
Each clown would have 3 balloons.

Which is right?

27 ÷ 9 = 3   60 ÷ 6 = 10   64 ÷ 8 = 8
36 ÷ 9 = 4   24 ÷ 4 = 6   28 ÷ 4 = 7